AQA GCSE Chemistry Lab Book

Contents

Published by Pearson Education Limited, 80 Strand, London, WC2R 0RL.
www.pearsonschoolsandfecolleges.co.uk

Text © Iain Brand, Nigel Saunders, Sue Robilliard and Pearson Education Limited 2017
Typeset and illustrated by Tech-Set Ltd Gateshead
Original illustrations © Pearson Education Limited 2015
Cover design by Pete Stratton
Cover photo/illustration © Shutterstock/CK Foto

First published 2017
19 18 17
10 9 8 7 6 5 4 3 2 1

British Library Cataloguing in Publication Data
A catalogue record for this book is available from the British Library

ISBN 978 1 292 230 986

Printed in Italy by Lego S.p.A.

Acknowledgements
The publishers would like to thank John Kavanagh for his contributions to the text.
The rights of Iain Brand, Nigel Saunders and Sue Robilliard to be identified as authors of this work have been asserted by them in accordance with the Copyright, Designs and Patents Act 1988.

Having an investigative mind and carrying out experiments is fundamental to science. The AQA science curriculum has carefully selected practical work to:

- enhance the delivered content
- increase enthusiasm for the subject
- promote a more scientifically literate society
- enable students to gain vital transferable skills.

Completing these required practicals, along with other investigations selected by your teacher, enables you to have a rich hands-on experience of science as it is meant to be – a dynamic, practical subject relevant to everyone.

This Lab Book has been designed to support your practical work, giving all the instructions you need to perform the required practicals, including apparatus and techniques (AT) skills self-assessment so that you can track your progress.

Every effort has been made to ensure coverage of the specification skills (WS – Working scientifically, AT – Use of apparatus and techniques), however, any method presented prevents fully completing WS 2.2 (Planning an investigation). WS 2.2 can also be covered if you plan an investigation prior to seeing the method presented. You can carry out your own plan, or adapt your plan using the method presented. Again, plans need to be risked assessed. It is hoped that the required practicals presented here are supplemented with other investigations and experiments that you complete through your GCSE course.

Salts, such as copper sulfate, are compounds formed by reacting an acid with a base. Copper oxide reacts with warm sulfuric acid to produce a blue solution of the salt copper sulfate. In this practical, you will use these reactants to prepare pure, dry, hydrated copper sulfate crystals.

Aim

To prepare a sample of pure, dry, hydrated copper sulfate crystals from copper oxide.

Apparatus

- safety goggles
- 250 cm³ beaker
- 100 cm³ beaker
- Bunsen burner
- gauze and tripod
- heatproof mat
- Petri dish or watch glass
- 100 cm³ measuring cylinder
- evaporating basin
- spatula
- stirring rod
- filter funnel
- filter paper
- tongs
- dilute sulfuric acid
- copper(II) oxide

Safety

Wear safety goggles at all times.

Your teacher may watch to see if you can:

- safely and correctly use apparatus.

AT links		Done
2	Safe use of appropriate heating devices and techniques including use of a Bunsen burner and a water bath or electric heater.	
3	Use of appropriate apparatus and techniques for conducting chemical reactions, including appropriate reagents.	
4	Safe use of a range of equipment to purify and/or separate chemical mixtures including evaporation, filtration, crystallisation.	
6	Safe use and careful handling of liquids and solids, including careful mixing of reagents under controlled conditions.	

Method

A Wearing goggles, pour about 40 cm³ of dilute sulfuric acid into a beaker.

B Set up the gauze, tripod and heatproof mat. Using the Bunsen burner, heat the acid *gently* until it is almost boiling. Turn off the Bunsen burner.

C Use the spatula to add a little copper oxide to the acid and stir.

D Keep adding small amounts of copper oxide until the black powder does not disappear after stirring. (This makes sure the copper oxide is in excess.)

E Filter the mixture into a beaker and pour into an evaporating basin.

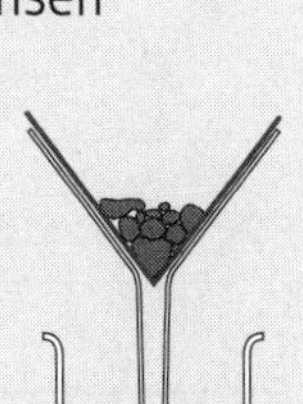

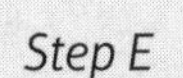

Step E

F Place the evaporating basin on top of a beaker half full of water. Heat the beaker, evaporating basin and contents using a Bunsen burner on a blue flame.

G Heat until about half of the water has evaporated. Then allow the evaporating basin to cool.

H When cool, transfer the solution to a Petri dish or watch glass and leave for a few days to allow the water to evaporate.

I Observe the shape and colour of the copper sulfate crystals formed.

Step F

Recording your results

1 Describe the colour, shape and size of the copper sulfate crystals produced.

....

....

2 Describe the appearance of:

a the sulfuric acid

b the copper oxide

c the solution at the end of the reaction.

Considering your results

3 Write a word equation to show the reaction you have carried out.

4 State why you need to be sure excess copper oxide is added in step **D**.

....

5 Name the substance left in the filter paper in step **E**.

6 What is dissolved in the solution that went through the filter paper?

7 Explain why this is an example of a neutralisation reaction.

....

....

8 What substance acts as a base in this reaction?

9 Write a symbol equation to show the reaction you have carried out. Include the state symbols.
Use your answer to question **3** to help you.

Titrations are used to find the exact volume of one solution that reacts with a fixed volume of another solution. The fixed volume of solution, often 25.0 cm^3, is measured in a pipette and the other solution is contained in a burette. These pieces of apparatus give accurate measurements. A burette has a fine scale, which gives it a good resolution: it can be read to the nearest half division (i.e. to 0.05 cm^3). Remember that the measuring instruments are calibrated for readings taken from the bottom of the meniscus.

In this practical, you will carry out an acid–alkali titration to determine the exact volume of acid needed to neutralise a given volume of alkali.

Aim

To find the volume of hydrochloric acid needed to neutralise 25.0 cm^3 of 0.10 $mol\,dm^{-3}$ sodium hydroxide solution.

Apparatus

- eye protection
- burette and stand
- funnel
- pipette and filler
- conical flask
- white tile
- wash bottle of distilled or deionised water
- methyl orange indicator
- 0.10 $mol\,dm^{-3}$ sodium hydroxide solution
- hydrochloric acid of unknown concentration

Safety

Eye protection must be worn.
Use a pipette filler.

Your teacher may watch to see if you can:

- follow instructions
- make accurate measurements.

AT links		Done
1	Use of appropriate apparatus to make and record a range of measurements accurately, including volume of liquids.	
8	The determination of concentrations of strong acids and strong alkalis.	

Method

A Place a funnel in the top of the burette, then rinse and fill the burette with the dilute hydrochloric acid.

B Fill the jet below the tap by running some acid out of the burette. Then remove the funnel from the top of the burette. Record the initial reading on the burette.

C Following instructions from your teacher, use the pipette filler to rinse and fill the pipette to the 25.0 cm^3 mark with the sodium hydroxide solution.

D Empty the sodium hydroxide solution from the pipette into a conical flask.

E Add a few drops of methyl orange to the conical flask, until the solution is yellow. Then place the flask on a white tile under the burette.

F Add the hydrochloric acid to the sodium hydroxide solution in small portions while swirling the conical flask.

G Stop adding the hydrochloric acid when the indicator turns a peach/orange colour. Record the burette reading. This is the rough titration to give you an approximate volume of hydrochloric acid needed. If the indicator turns pink, you have added too much hydrochloric acid.

H Repeat steps **A** to **E** (except for rinsing the burette and pipette). Add hydrochloric acid to the sodium hydroxide until you have used 1 cm^3 less than in the rough titration. Use a wash bottle of distilled/deionised water to rinse the tip of the burette with a little water to make sure no hydrochloric acid is left there. Then add hydrochloric acid drop by drop until the solution in the flask is peach/orange. Record the burette reading.

I Repeat step **H** until you have two concordant results (within 0.2 cm^3 of each other).

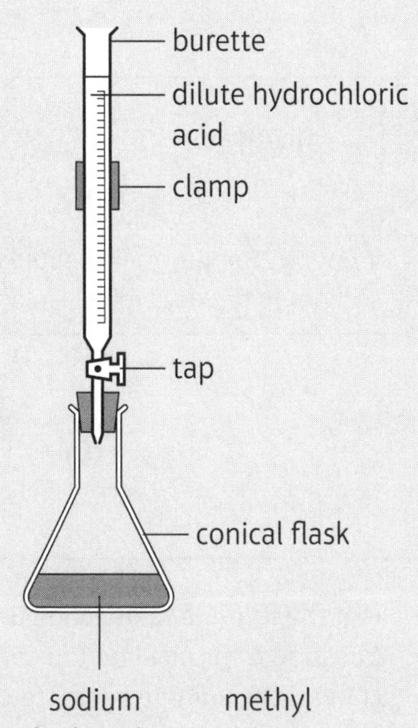

Results

1 Record your results in the table below.

Burette reading	Titration 1	Titration 2	Titration 3	Titration 4	Titration 5
Final reading (cm^3)					
Initial reading (cm^3)					
Volume added (cm^3)					

Conclusion

2 Calculate the mean of the concordant results (results that are within 0.2 cm^3 of each other).

3 Calculate the number of moles of sodium hydroxide in 25.0 cm^3 of 0.10 $mol\,dm^{-3}$ sodium hydroxide solution. Use the formula:

number of moles of solute = volume of solution (dm^3) × concentration ($mol\,dm^{-3}$)

Remember to convert the volume in cm^3 to dm^3 by dividing by 1000.

4 The equation for the reaction between hydrochloric acid and sodium hydroxide is:

$$HCl + NaOH \rightarrow NaCl + H_2O$$

Work out the number of moles of hydrochloric acid that reacted with the number of moles of sodium hydroxide you calculated in question **3**.

5 Use the formula in question **3**, the mean volume of hydrochloric acid and your answer to question **4** to calculate the concentration of hydrochloric acid in $mol\,dm^{-3}$. Remember to convert the volume in cm^3 to dm^3.

The electrolysis of molten or dissolved ionic salts is carried out using inert (unreactive) electrodes (usually graphite or platinum). When a molten salt is electrolysed, ions are discharged as atoms or molecules at the electrodes. However, electrolysis of dissolved ionic salts is more complex. This is because water ionises to a very small extent, so in an aqueous solution of a salt there are some hydrogen ions (H^+) and hydroxide ions (OH^-), as well as the ions of the dissolved solid. You are going to predict the substances formed at electrodes when different substances are electrolysed. You will then carry out the electrolysis of these substances to confirm whether you were right.

Your teacher may watch to see if you can:

- follow instructions carefully
- work safely.

AT links		Done
3	Use of appropriate apparatus and techniques for conducting and monitoring chemical reactions.	
7	Use of appropriate apparatus and techniques to draw, set up and use electrochemical cells for separation and production of elements and compounds.	
8	Use of appropriate qualititative reagents and techniques to analyse and identify unknown samples or products including gas tests for hydrogen, oxygen and chlorine.	

Aim

To investigate the substances that are formed at the electrodes when different salt solutions are electrolysed.

Apparatus

- safety goggles
- copper(II) sulfate solution
- sodium chloride solution
- carbon electrodes
- 100 cm³ beaker
- Petri dish lid
- tweezers
- connecting leads
- copper(II) chloride solution
- sodium sulfate solution
- low voltage power supply
- damp litmus paper
- electrode holder

Safety

Safety goggles need to be worn throughout the practical.

Hypothesis

Write down your hypothesis. Explain why you made this hypothesis.

Prediction

Now that you have studied electrolysis, predict what products will be formed at each electrode and give reasons for your predictions.

Solution	Positive electrode	Negative electrode	Why I think this...
copper(II) chloride			(positive electrode)
			(negative electrode)
copper(II) sulfate			(positive electrode)
			(negative electrode)
sodium chloride			(positive electrode)
			(negative electrode)
sodium sulfate			(positive electrode)
			(negative electrode)

Method

A Place about 50 cm^3 of copper(II) chloride solution into a 100 cm^3 beaker.

B Insert the carbon electrodes into the electrode holder and place this into the copper(II) chloride solution.

C Use the leads to connect the electrodes to the low voltage power supply. Make sure you connect the electrodes to the d.c. terminals. These are normally coloured red and black.

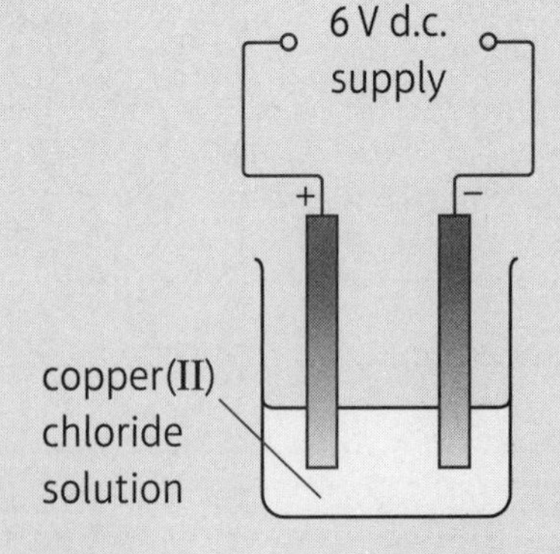

D Set the voltage to 6 V and switch on.

E Look at the electrodes. Is anything happening? There could be a colour change or fizzing.

F Hold a piece of damp litmus paper close to the electrode that is bubbling. (This should be the positive electrode.) What do you see happening? Add this information to your results table on the next page.

G After a few minutes, switch off the low voltage supply and take a closer look at the other electrode. (This should be the negative electrode.) Is there a colour change? Record any information in your results table.

H Remove the liquid from the beaker. Your teacher will tell you where to put this. You will need to clean both electrodes. Rinsing them under running water should be fine.

I Repeat steps **A** to **H** using the other solutions.

Considering your results/conclusions

1 Make sure your table below is complete. Don't forget to write in your evidence.

Solution	Positive electrode	Negative electrode	Evidence for this...
copper(II) chloride			(positive electrode)
			(negative electrode)
copper(II) sulfate			(positive electrode)
			(negative electrode)
sodium chloride			(positive electrode)
			(negative electrode)
sodium sulfate			(positive electrode)
			(negative electrode)

2 Compare your final results with the predictions you made at the start. How accurate were your predictions?

....

....

3 The test for chlorine is that it bleaches damp litmus paper. The other two gases you are likely to have found would need additional tests to confirm what they are. Write down the names of these gases and the tests for them.

....

....

....

....

....

During a chemical reaction, energy is transferred between the reacting substances and their surroundings. This energy transfer is usually by heating, particularly if a reaction takes place in solution. The stored thermal (heat) energy in the solution increases during an exothermic reaction, and decreases during an endothermic reaction. This means you can determine whether a reaction in solution is exothermic or endothermic:

- the temperature increases in an exothermic reaction
- the temperature decreases in an endothermic reaction.

You are going to investigate a type of reaction known as a neutralisation reaction.

Your teacher may watch to see if you can:

- follow instructions carefully
- work safely.

AT links		Done
1	Use of appropriate apparatus to make and record a range of measurements accurately, including mass, temperature, and volume of liquids.	
3	Use of appropriate apparatus and techniques for conducting and monitoring chemical reactions.	
5	Making and recording of appropriate observations during chemical reactions including changes in temperature.	
6	Safe use and careful handling of gases, liquids and solids, including careful mixing of reagents under controlled conditions, using appropriate apparatus to explore chemical changes.	

Aim

To react hydrochloric acid with sodium hydroxide solution in a neutralisation reaction and measure the temperature change.

Apparatus

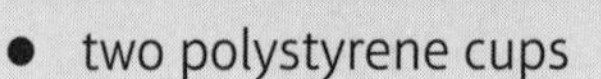

- two polystyrene cups
- 250 cm³ beaker
- lid for one cup
- measuring cylinders
- sodium hydroxide
- hydrochloric acid
- tripod
- thermometer
- safety goggles

Safety ⚠

Wear safety goggles.

Sodium hydroxide and hydrochloric acid at this concentration are corrosive and very damaging to eyes.

Hypothesis

Write down your hypothesis for this experiment. This hypothesis could include a sketch graph.

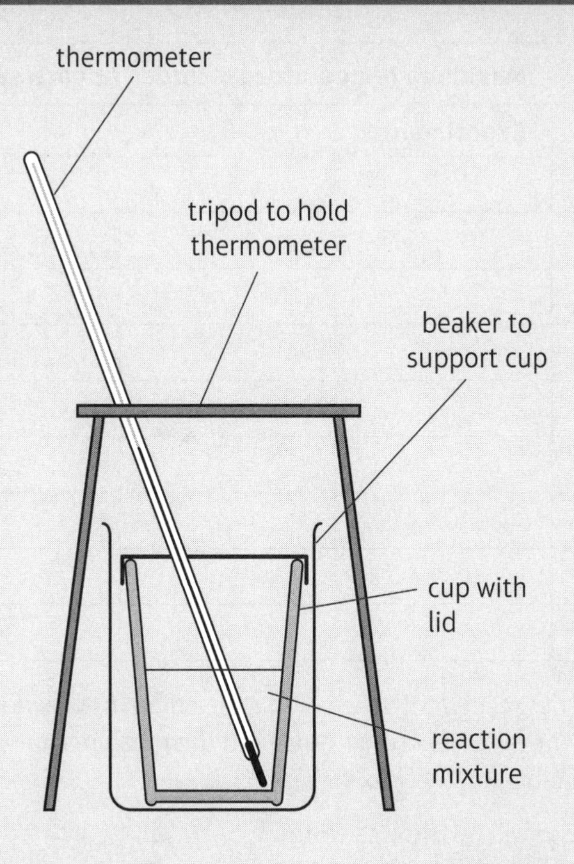

Method

A Use a measuring cylinder to put 30 cm^3 of 2.0 mol/dm^3 hydrochloric acid into a polystyrene cup.

B Clean out the measuring cylinder with water.

C Place the polystyrene cup into a glass beaker to make it more stable. Take the temperature of the acid and write this in your results table. This should go in the column for experiment 1.

D Use the measuring cylinder to put 40 cm^3 of 2.0 mol/dm^3 sodium hydroxide solution into a second polystyrene cup.

E Remove 5 cm^3 of 2.0 mol/dm^3 sodium hydroxide solution from your 40 cm^3 measured out in step **D**.

F Add this to the polystyrene cup containing the acid. Put the lid on the cup containing the mixture and stir with the thermometer. Enclose the thermometer with a tripod to stop the cup and thermometer falling over.

G Keep stirring until the temperature reaches a maximum and starts to fall. Record the highest temperature in your table.

H Repeat steps **E** to **G** until all the 40 cm^3 of sodium hydroxide solution has been added.

I When you have finished, rinse out your cups and measuring cylinders and repeat the experiment at least one more time. If time is short, you could use results from other groups because everyone will have used the same amounts and the same strengths of solutions.

Considering your results/conclusions

1 Record your results in the table on the following page. There are some extra columns for repeated results from your experiments or results from other groups. To calculate the mean, add up all the results in a row and divide by the number of results in the row.

Volume of sodium hydroxide solution added (cm^3)	Maximum temperature recorded at each stage (°C)				
	Experiment 1	**Experiment 2**			**Mean**
0					
5					
10					
15					
20					
25					
30					
35					
40					

2 On the next page, draw a graph of your results with the volume of sodium hydroxide solution added (cm^3)(the independent variable) on the *x*-axis and the mean maximum temperature (°C)(the dependent variable) on the *y*-axis.

3 Draw two straight lines of best fit. One will be through all the points which are increasing in temperature and the other will be through all the points which are decreasing in temperature. You need to make sure the lines cross, so you might need to extend them. The diagram to the right should give you an idea what this should look like.

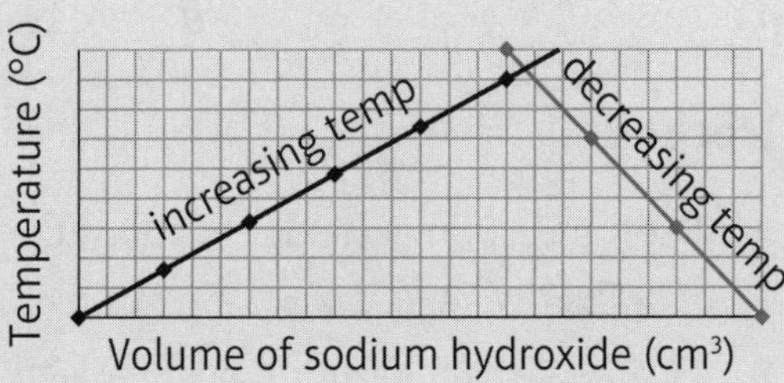

4 What volumes of hydrochloric acid and sodium hydroxide would produce the largest temperature rise?

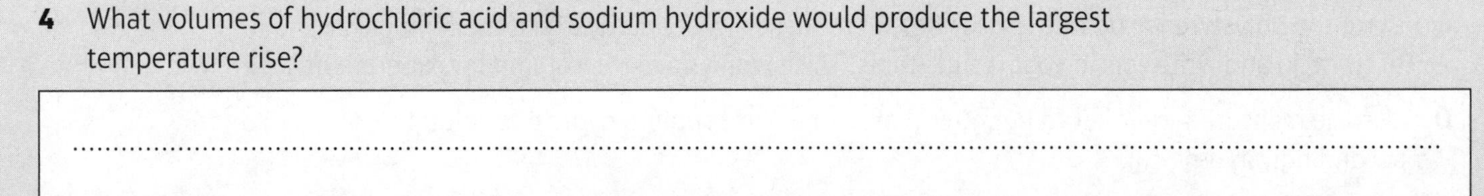

5 Why does the temperature start to fall towards the end of the experiment?

....

Evaluation

6 How could you make the data you collect from this investigation more accurate?

....

7 It is difficult to find the exact volume of sodium hydroxide solution that would give the maximum temperature rise. What further work would you need to carry out to find this exact volume of sodium hydroxide?

....

....

The progress of a chemical reaction can be measured by how the amounts of reactant or product change with time, or by the time taken for the reaction to reach a certain point.

You are going to investigate the reaction between hydrochloric acid and marble chips (calcium carbonate), to find out how the concentration of the acid affects the rate. You will monitor the progress of the reaction by measuring the volume of carbon dioxide produced.

Aim

To investigate the effect on the rate of reaction of changing the concentration of solutions by measuring the production of a gas.

Apparatus

- eye protection
- balance
- water trough
- 100 cm^3 measuring cylinder
- stop clock
- conical flask
- delivery tube and bung
- marble chips
- 1.0 mol/dm^3 and 2.0 mol/dm^3 hydrochloric acid

Safety

Wear eye protection at all times.

Care is needed with acid solutions. Wash off splashes immediately.

AT links		Done
1	Use of appropriate apparatus to make and record a range of measurements accurately, including mass, temperature, and volume of liquids.	
3	Use of appropriate apparatus and techniques for conducting and monitoring chemical reactions.	
5	Making and recording of appropriate observations during chemical reactions including changes in temperature.	
6	Safe use and careful handling of gases, liquids and solids, including careful mixing of reagents under controlled conditions, using appropriate apparatus to explore chemical changes.	

Part 1: Measuring gas production

Your teacher may watch to see if you can:

- carefully control variables during investigations
- measure change accurately.

Hypothesis

Write down your hypothesis. Explain your hypothesis.

....

....

....

....

....

....

Method

A Set up the apparatus as shown in the diagram.

B Measure 40 cm^3 of 2.0 mol/dm^3 hydrochloric acid into a conical flask.

C Add 5 g of marble chips to the flask.

D Immediately stopper the flask and start the stop clock.

E Note the total volume of gas produced after every 30 seconds for five minutes or until the reaction has finished.

F Repeat steps **A** to **E** using 1.0 mol/dm^3 hydrochloric acid.

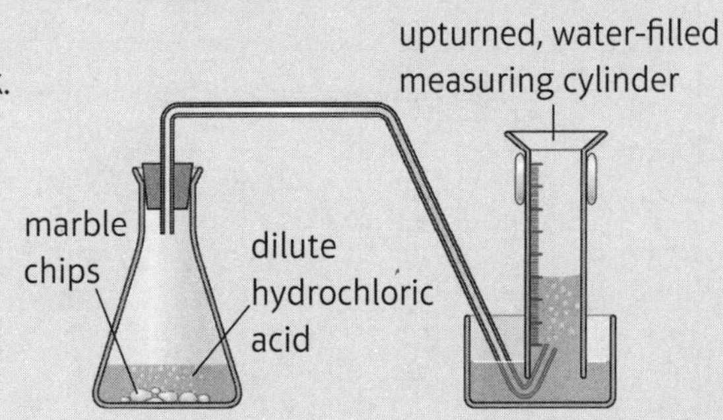

Recording your results

1 Record your results in the table below.

Time (min)	**0**	**0.5**	**1.0**	**1.5**	**2.0**	**2.5**	**3.0**	**3.5**	**4.0**	**4.5**	**5.0**
Volume of gas produced using 2.0 mol/dm^3 hydrochloric acid (cm^3)											
Volume of gas produced using 1.0 mol/dm^3 hydrochloric acid (cm^3)											

Considering your results/conclusion

2 Draw a scatter diagram for both sets of results on the same graph. The volume of gas produced in cm^3 (the dependent variable) should be on the *y*-axis. The time in minutes (the independent variable) should be on the *x*-axis. Use different coloured lines for the two concentrations of acid.

3 Explain how you can tell from the scatter diagrams when the reactions were finished.

4 Describe how increasing the concentration affects the rate of reaction.

5 Explain how your results and scatter diagrams fit with your conclusion in question **4**.

Evaluation

6 Suggest possible sources of error in this investigation.

7 Suggest possible changes to the method that could improve the reliability of the results.

Part 2: Observing a colour change

The progress of a chemical reaction can be measured by how amounts of reactant or product change with time, or by the time taken for the reaction to reach a certain point.

You are going to investigate the effect of concentration on the rate of reaction between sodium thiosulfate and hydrochloric acid. You will monitor the progress of the reaction by observing a colour change.

Aim

To investigate the effect of changing the concentration on the rate of reaction between sodium thiosulfate and hydrochloric acid, by observing a colour change in the solutions.

Apparatus 

- eye protection
- 250 cm^3 conical flask
- 10 cm^3 measuring cylinder
- 50 cm^3 measuring cylinder
- stop clock
- test tube
- test tube rack
- white paper with cross
- sodium thiosulfate solution
- dilute hydrochloric acid

Safety 

Wear eye protection at all times.

Care is needed with acid solutions. Wash off splashes immediately.

Take care to avoid breathing in any sulfur dioxide fumes.

Your teacher may watch to see if you can:

- carefully control variables during investigations
- measure change accurately
- work safely.

Hypothesis

Write down your hypothesis. Explain your hypothesis.

Method

A Place 10 cm^3 of sodium thiosulfate solution and 40 cm^3 of water into a 250 cm^3 conical flask.

B Measure 10 cm^3 of dilute hydrochloric acid into a measuring cylinder.

C Place the conical flask (containing the previously measured out sodium thiosulfate and water) on a piece of white paper marked with a cross, as shown opposite.

D Add the acid to the thiosulfate and start the stop clock.

E Looking down from above, stop the clock when the cross disappears.

F Note this time.

G Repeat steps **A** to **F**, replacing the original amounts of sodium thiosulfate and water in step **A** with the following:

- 20 cm^3 sodium thiosulfate + 30 cm^3 water
- 30 cm^3 sodium thiosulfate + 20 cm^3 water
- 40 cm^3 sodium thiosulfate + 10 cm^3 water
- 50 cm^3 sodium thiosulfate + no water

H Repeat the entire investigation to obtain a second set of results. If time is short, your teacher may suggest that you share results with other groups instead.

Recording your results

1 Record your results in the table below. The final column has the concentrations of sodium thiosulfate worked out for you (providing you used the suggested amounts of water and sodium thiosulfate). This will help you with later questions.

Volume of sodium thiosulfate (cm^3)	Volume of water (cm^3)	Time taken for cross to disappear from view (seconds)				Concentration of sodium thiosulfate (g/dm^3)
		Experiment 1	Experiment 2	Experiment 3	Mean	
10	40					8
20	30					16
30	20					24
40	10					32
50	0					40

Considering your results/conclusion

2 Draw a scatter diagram with mean time taken for the cross to disappear from view, in seconds (the dependent variable) on the *y*-axis and sodium thiosulfate concentration in g/dm^3 (the independent variable) on the *x*-axis. Draw a smooth curved line of best fit.

3 **a** Describe how concentration affects the rate of this reaction.

....

....

....

....

....

b Explain your answer to part **a** by referring to the shape of your scatter diagram.

....

....

....

....

....

4 If the rate of reaction doubled, what would happen to the time taken for the cross to disappear?

....

....

....

....

....

5 Compare your results with other groups. How similar are they? Does this mean the investigation is reproducible?

....

....

....

....

....

....

....

....

....

6 Compare your results from Parts 1 and 2. Both investigations looked at the effect of changing concentration, using different methods to measure the rate of reaction. Can you see a similar pattern in both investigations?

....

....

....

....

....

....

....

....

....

Evaluation

7 a Describe two possible sources of error in this investigation.

....

....

....

....

....

....

....

....

b Suggest a way of reducing one of these errors.

....

....

....

....

....

....

....

....

Many inks contain a mixture of dyes. Chromatography can be used to identify inks; for example, inks from crime scenes or from documents that may have been forged. You are going to carry out an experiment using paper chromatography. You will then use the results to calculate R_f values.

Aim

To test some inks to see how many dyes they contain and calculate their R_f values.

Apparatus

- pencil and ruler
- beaker
- chromatography paper attached to a pencil, rod or splint
- two marker pens or felt-tip pens

Your teacher may watch to see if you can:

- follow instructions carefully
- draw conclusions from your results.

AT links		Done
1	Use of appropriate apparatus to make and record a range of measurements accurately.	
4	Safe use of a range of equipment to purify and/or separate chemical mixtures including chromatography.	

Method

A Check that your chromatography paper hangs close to the bottom of the empty beaker without touching it (as shown in the diagram).

B Take the paper out of the beaker and draw a pencil line on the paper, about 2 cm from the bottom.

C Put a small spot of ink from each pen on your pencil line.

D Write the name of each pen or ink below each spot with a pencil.

E Pour some water into the beaker to a depth of about 1 cm.

F Lower the chromatography paper into the beaker so that the bottom of the paper is in the water, but the water level is below the spots (see the diagram).

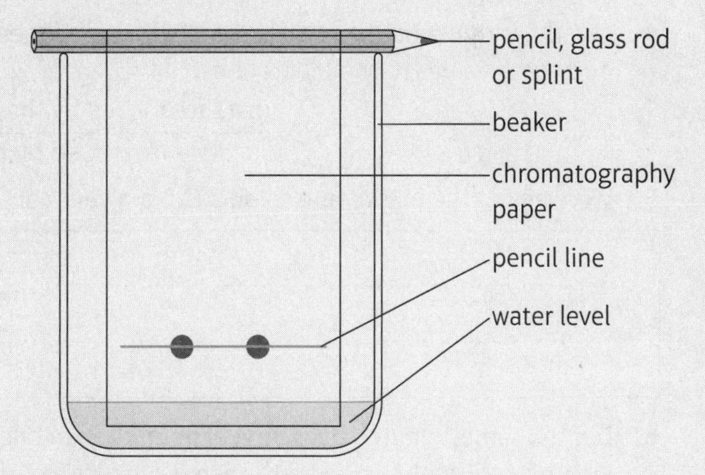

G Leave the paper in the beaker until the water has soaked up the paper almost to the top. The water is the solvent for the different coloured dye compounds in the inks. The solvent is called the mobile phase in chromatography, because it is the part that moves.

H Take the paper out and immediately use a pencil to mark the location of the solvent front (the level the water reached) before it evaporates. Leave the paper to dry.

Recording your results

1 Describe the coloured dye compounds that mixed to produce the ink in each pen.

....

....

....

....

....

....

2 Measure the distance the solvent (the water) has risen from the pencil line.

3 Measure the distance that each dye spot has risen from the pencil line (i.e. measure from the pencil line to the top of each different coloured spot). Write your results in the tables below.

Name of pen/ink:				
Colours of dye spots				
Distance of spot from pencil line (cm)				
R_f value (see below for formula)				

Name of pen/ink:				
Colours of dye spots				
Distance of spot from pencil line (cm)				
R_f value (see below for formula)				

Considering your results/conclusions

4 Use the formula below to calculate the R_f value for each separate colour in the two inks. Add these values to the tables above.

$$R_f = \frac{\text{distance moved by the coloured spot}}{\text{distance moved by the solvent}}$$

5 Were any of the inks a pure colour? Explain your conclusion.

....

....

6 Did the same coloured dyes appear in more than one ink? If so, do you think they were the same chemical compound? Explain your answer.

....

....

Evaluation

7 Why was the starting line drawn in pencil?

....

8 Why did you have to label the spots?

....

9 Why is the chromatography paper hung with the bottom just in the water?

....

Analytical chemists use different techniques to determine which substances are present or absent.

Different metal cations produce different flame test colours. Flame tests work with solid samples and with solutions, but flame colours from solids are easier to see. You will complete flame tests on known substances before using these results to identify some unknown chemicals.

Aim 

To determine the flame test colours for lithium, sodium, potassium, copper and calcium ions, and use flame tests to identify the metal ions in different unknown solids.

Apparatus 

- eye protection
- Bunsen burner
- heat-resistant mat
- flame test loop
- beaker
- dilute hydrochloric acid
- test tubes
- test tube rack
- known solids
- unknown solids

Safety

Wear eye protection.

Hydrochloric acid and test solutions are irritants.

Substances on the flame test loop may spit when in the Bunsen burner flame.

Close the air hole between tests to give a luminous flame.

Your teacher may watch to see if you can:

- carry out an experiment appropriately
- use apparatus accurately and safely.

AT links		Done
1	Safe use of a Bunsen burner.	
8	Use of appropriate qualitative reagents and techniques to analyse and identify unknown samples or products including gas tests, flame tests and precipitation reactions.	

Cleaning the flame test loop

A Light the Bunsen burner and open the air hole to give a hot blue flame.

B Dip the flame test loop into the dilute hydrochloric acid. Hold the loop in the flame, then dip it in a beaker of water.

C If you see an intense flame colour in step **B**, repeat step **B** until you see only a faint flame colour (or no colour).

Determining flame test colours

D Dip the clean flame test loop into one of the five known solids (containing Li^+, Na^+, K^+, Cu^{2+} or Ca^{2+} ions).

E Hold the loop in the edge of a hot blue flame, as shown in the diagram. Observe and record the flame test colour in the table below.

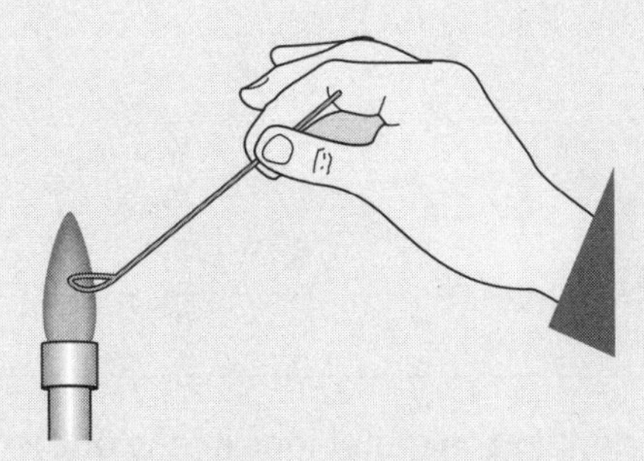

F Repeat steps **D** and **E** with the other known solids, remembering to clean the loop before each test.

Identifying metal ions

G Carry out flame tests on the five unknown solids. Observe and record each flame test colour.

Recording your results

Record the flame test colours of the known and unknown solids in the tables below.

Metal ion	Flame test colour
lithium, Li^+	
sodium, Na^+	
potassium, K^+	
copper, Cu^{2+}	
calcium, Ca^{2+}	

Unknown	Flame test colour
1	
2	
3	
4	
5	

Considering your results/conclusions

1 Use the flame test colours to identify the metal ions in each unknown solid. Complete the table.

Unknown	Metal ion
1	
2	
3	
4	
5	

Evaluation

2 Explain why you need to clean the flame test loop between the different flame tests.

....

....

....

....

....

....

....

....

....

....

....

3 Explain whether it was difficult to identify the metal ions in any of the unknown solids.

....

....

....

....

....

....

....

....

....

....

....

Analytical chemists use different techniques to determine which substances are present or absent.

Precipitation reactions involving sodium hydroxide solution form the basis of a test to identify dissolved metal ions. Sodium hydroxide solution forms different coloured precipitates with certain dissolved metal compounds. You are going to use this test to identify the metal ions in some unknown substances.

Aim

To use dilute sodium hydroxide solution to identify metal ions in solution.

To find out the metal hydroxide precipitate colours for aluminium, calcium, copper, iron(II) and iron(III) ions and use these tests to identify the metal ions in different unknown solutions.

Apparatus

- eye protection
- dropping pipettes
- test tubes
- test tube rack
- dilute sodium hydroxide solution
- known solutions
- unknown solutions

Safety

Wear eye protection.

Sodium hydroxide solution is an irritant. Avoid skin contact.

Your teacher may watch to see if you can:

- carry out an experiment appropriately
- use apparatus accurately and safely.

Determining metal hydroxide precipitate colours

A Using a dropping pipette, fill a test tube to a depth of about 2 cm with one of the five known solutions (containing Al^{3+}, Ca^{2+}, Cu^{2+}, Fe^{2+} or Fe^{3+} ions).

B Using a different dropping pipette, add a few drops of sodium hydroxide solution to the tube. Hold the test tube near the top and shake the bottom gently from side to side to mix its contents.

C Observe and record the colour of the precipitate produced.

D If a white precipitate forms in step **C**, add more sodium hydroxide solution until the test tube is about half full. Observe and record whether the precipitate disappears to leave a colourless solution.

E Repeat steps **A** to **D** with the other known solutions. Do not contaminate one solution with another.

Identifying metal ions

F Carry out steps **A** to **D** on each of the five unknown solutions. Observe and record the colour of each precipitate and whether any white precipitate formed disappears when excess sodium hydroxide solution is added.

Recording your results

1 Record the precipitate colours of the known and unknown solutions in the tables below.

Metal ion	Precipitate colour	Effect of adding excess sodium hydroxide
aluminium, Al^{3+}		
calcium, Ca^{2+}		
copper, Cu^{2+}		
iron(II), Fe^{2+}		
iron(III), Fe^{3+}		

Unknown	Precipitate colour
1	
2	
3	
4	
5	

Considering your results/conclusions

2 Use your results to identify the metal ions present in each unknown solution.
Complete the table.

Unknown	Metal ion
1	
2	
3	
4	
5	

Evaluation

3 Explain why step **D** is needed to identify some metal ions in solution.

....

....

....

....

....

....

....

....

....

....

....

....

....

....

....

....

Analytical chemists use different techniques to determine which substances are present or absent.

In this practical you will identify halide ions, sulfate ions or carbonate ions.

Aim

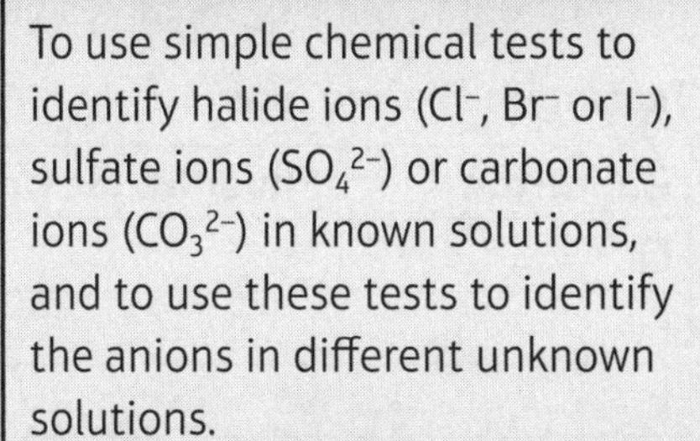

To use simple chemical tests to identify halide ions (Cl^-, Br^- or I^-), sulfate ions (SO_4^{2-}) or carbonate ions (CO_3^{2-}) in known solutions, and to use these tests to identify the anions in different unknown solutions.

Apparatus

- eye protection
- dropping pipettes
- test tubes
- test tube rack
- dilute nitric acid
- silver nitrate solution
- dilute hydrochloric acid
- barium chloride solution
- known solutions
- unknown solutions

Safety

Wear eye protection and avoid skin contact with the substances used.

Barium chloride solution is harmful.

Dilute nitric acid is an irritant.

Your teacher may watch to see if you can:

- use apparatus accurately and safely.

Testing for halide ions

A Fill a test tube to a depth of about 2 cm with one of the solutions containing halide ions (Cl^-, Br^- or I^- ions).

B Add a few drops of dilute nitric acid. Hold the tube near the top and shake the bottom gently from side to side to mix its contents.

C Add a few drops of silver nitrate solution. Record the colour of the precipitate produced.

D Repeat steps **A** to **C** with the other known solutions that contain halide ions (Cl^-, Br^- or I^- ions).

Testing for sulfate ions

E Fill a test tube to a depth of about 2 cm with the solution containing sulfate ions, SO_4^{2-}.

F Add a few drops of dilute hydrochloric acid. Hold the tube near the top and shake the bottom gently from side to side to mix its contents.

G Add a few drops of barium chloride solution. Record the colour of the precipitate produced.

Testing for carbonate ions

H Fill a test tube to a depth of about 2 cm with the solution containing carbonate ions, CO_3^{2-}.

I Add a few drops of dilute hydrochloric acid. Record whether bubbling occurs.

Identifying negative ions in solution

J Fill a test tube to a depth of about 2 cm with one of the unknown solutions.

K Carry out a test for halide ions or sulfate ions. Also look for bubbling (which indicates the presence of carbonate ions) when you acidify the solution with dilute nitric acid or with dilute hydrochloric acid.

L Repeat steps **J** and **K** until you have determined which negative ions are present in each of the unknown solutions.

Recording your results

Record your results in the tables below.

Testing for halide ions

Halide ion	Silver halide precipitate colour
Cl^-	
Br^-	
I^-	

Unknown	Observations
1	
2	
3	
4	
5	

Testing for sulfate ions

Sulfate ion	Precipitate colour
SO_4^{2-}	

Unknown	Observations
1	
2	
3	
4	
5	

Testing for carbonate ions

Carbonate ion	Bubbling visible (yes/no)
CO_3^{2-}	

Unknown	Observations
1	
2	
3	
4	
5	

Considering your results/conclusions

1 Use your results to identify the negative ions in each unknown solution. Complete the table below.

Unknown	Negative ion
1	
2	
3	
4	
5	

Evaluation

2 Silver carbonate and barium carbonate are insoluble solids. Suggest why dilute acids are added to the test solutions in steps **B** and **F**.

....

....

....

....

....

Water is one of our most valuable raw materials. It is used in washing and cleaning as well as agriculture and industry. Probably its most important use is for drinking. Around the world, there is a need to ensure that water provided is fit to drink. This is known as potable water. In your investigation, you will test a sample of water before and after distilling it to see if you have managed to produce potable water.

Aim

To produce potable water from a provided salty water sample and to complete tests on the water sample before and after distillation to prove it is now pure water.

Apparatus

- salty water sample
- nitric acid
- silver nitrate solution
- nichrome wire
- Bunsen burner
- heat-resistant mat
- test tubes

Your teacher may watch to see if you can:

- follow instructions carefully
- work safely.

AT links		Done
2	Safe use of appropriate heating devices and techniques including use of a Bunsen burner and a water bath or electric heater.	
4	Safe use of a range of equipment to purify and/or separate chemical mixtures including evaporation, distillation.	

Method 1: Pre-distillation and post-distillation

A Obtain approximately 1 cm depth of the salty water sample and put it into a test tube.

Flame test (metal ions)

B Carry out a flame test on this sample by dipping the nichrome wire into the sample and holding it in a blue Bunsen burner flame. The flame colour will indicate which substance (positive metal ion) is present in the sample. Record your results in the table on the following page.

Possible flame colours: **yellow** – sodium, **lilac** – potassium, **crimson** – lithium, **brick red** – calcium, **green** – barium

Nitric acid/Silver nitrate test (halide ions)

C Add 3–4 drops of dilute nitric acid to the remaining salty water sample in the test tube. Then add 1 cm depth of silver nitrate solution. The colour of the precipitate will indicate which substance (negative halide ion) is present in the sample. Record your results in the table on the following page.

Possible precipitate colours: **white –** chloride ions, **cream** – bromide ions, **yellow** – iodide ions

D Clean out the test tube and move on to Method 2: Distillation.

Method 2: Distillation

E Set up your apparatus as shown in the diagram. Clamp the conical flask to the tripod and gauze. Put anti-bumping granules in the bottom of the flask.

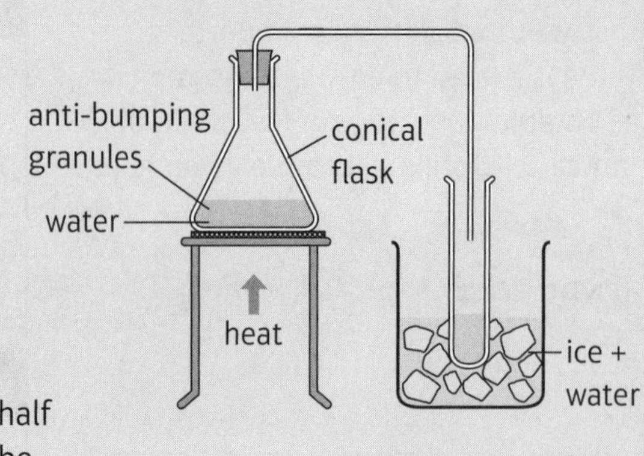

F Adjust the Bunsen burner so you have a gentle blue flame. The air hole should be about half open and the gas tap should be about half on. Heat the water until it boils.

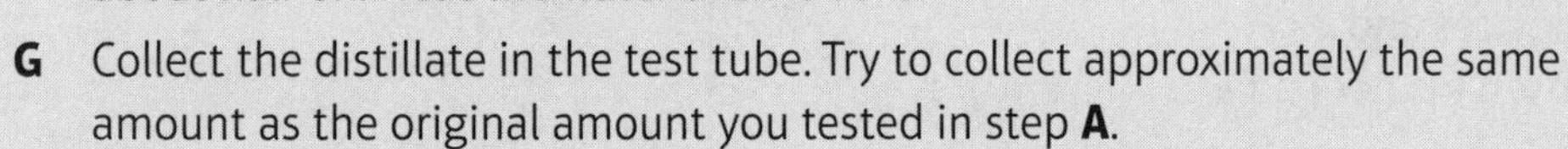

G Collect the distillate in the test tube. Try to collect approximately the same amount as the original amount you tested in step **A**.

H Repeat steps **A** to **D** on this newly distilled sample of water.

Apparatus

- salty water sample
- ice
- 250 cm^3 beaker
- 250 cm^3 conical flask
- clamp stand
- anti-bumping granules
- Bunsen burner
- tripod
- heat-resistant mat
- gauze
- delivery tube with bung

Safety

Wear eye protection.

Tie long hair back.

Considering your results/conclusions

1 Write your results in the table below.
(Hint: Remember what results you should have obtained if using a sample of 'salty water', i.e. sodium chloride solution.)

	Sample	**Flame test (positive metal ions)**	**Nitric acid/silver nitrate test (negative halide ions)**
Before	Salty water		
After	Distilled water		

2 Did you purify the water successfully? Explain your answer.

....

....

....

3 What other test could you carry out to show that the newly distilled sample is water?

....

....

Evaluation

4 Explain what happened when the salty water was distilled. In your explanation, use the following words: boil, evaporate, liquid, steam, temperature, vapour. Go on to a separate sheet of paper if you need to.

....

....

....

1 Making salts

1 The crystals are blue and diamond shaped. (The size will vary depending on conditions.)

2 a clear solution
  b black solid (powder)
  c blue solution

3 copper oxide + sulfuric acid → copper sulfate + water

4 So that all the acid is used up.

5 copper oxide

6 copper sulfate

7 This is known as a neutralisation reaction because the hydrogen ions of the acid are removed (and a salt and water are formed). The hydrogen ions make the initial solution acidic, but the final solution is neutral (because both the salt and water are neutral substances).

8 copper oxide

9 $CuO(s) + H_2SO_4(aq) \rightarrow CuSO_4(aq) + H_2O(l)$

2 Neutralisation

1–2 Your own results. (Your teacher will have the correct answers for the substances provided.)

3 Number of moles of NaOH = (25.0 ÷ 1000) × 0.10 = 0.0025

4 Number of moles of HCl = 0.0025

This is the same as the answer to Q3 because the ratio of NaOH to HCl is 1:1 – this is shown by the balanced symbol equation.

5 Concentration of HCl = (0.0025 ÷ mean volume HCl) × 1000

(If you convert cm^3 to dm^3 before doing the calculation, there is no need to multiply by 1000.)

3 Electrolysis

1

Solution	Positive electrode	Negative electrode	Evidence for this...
copper (II) chloride	chlorine	copper	(positive electrode) bubbling at electrode which bleaches damp litmus paper
			(negative electrode) brown/pink substance on electrode
copper (II) sulfate	oxygen	copper	(positive electrode) bubbling at electrode which doesn't bleach litmus paper
			(negative electrode) brown/pink substance on electrode
sodium chloride	chlorine	hydrogen	(positive electrode) bubbling at electrode which bleaches damp litmus paper
			(negative electrode) bubbling at electrode which doesn't bleach damp litmus paper
sodium sulfate	oxygen	hydrogen	(positive electrode) bubbling at electrode which doesn't bleach damp litmus paper
			(negative electrode) bubbling at electrode which doesn't bleach damp litmus paper

2 Your own comparisons.

3 Hydrogen gas: use a lit wooden splint/spill – it should go out with a pop.

Oxygen gas: use a glowing wooden splint/spill – it should relight.

4 Temperature changes

1–3 Your own results.

4 The volume of hydrochloric acid will be 30 cm^3 (as this is the initial volume and doesn't change). The volume of sodium hydroxide will depend on your graph – it should be volume at the point where the lines of best fit cross.

5 At this point, no reaction is taking place. The acid has been used up and sodium hydroxide is now in excess. It is this excess, colder, sodium hydroxide which lowers the temperature.

6 Use a digital temperature sensor so the reading can more easily be seen going up and down. (This will also increase the precision of the temperature readings.)

7 Look at your graph and find the region where the lines of best fit cross. Read off the volume of sodium hydroxide at this point. Repeat the investigation but add 1 cm^3 of sodium hydroxide at a time (rather than 5 cm^3), using volumes approximately 5 cm^3 either side of the maximum value read from your graph.

5 Rates of reaction

Part 1

1 Your own results.

2 Your own scatter diagram. Both curves of best fit should rise steadily and then level off at about the same point. The curve for the higher concentration of acid should rise and level off more quickly.

3 The reaction has finished at the point where the line on the scatter graph levels off and becomes horizontal.

4 Increasing the concentration increases the rate of the reaction (makes the reaction faster).

5 The higher acid concentration (2.0 mol/dm^3) produced a larger amount of gas in a shorter time, so the line drawn on the graph relating to these results was steeper at the start.

6 One possible source of error is measuring the volume of gas (which is difficult because of the bubbles in the measuring cylinder. Other answers are possible.)

7 Measure the volume of gas produced for a longer time, or measure larger volumes of gas. Other answers are possible.

Part 2

1 Your own results.

2 Your own graph. The scatter diagram should show a curve, starting high on the left (at a low concentration of sodium thiosulfate) and decreasing to the bottom right (at a high concentration of sodium thiosulfate).

3 a The rate increases quickly as the concentration of sodium thiosulfate increases.
  b The scatter diagram shows that the time for the reaction decreases as the concentration increases; this means the rate of reaction increases.

4 The time taken would halve.

5 Your own view, depending on other results.

6 Your own answer. Both experiments should show that increasing the concentration increases the rate of reaction.

7 Measurement of time and measurement of volume of solutions.

8 Errors with recording time could be reduced by repeating the experiment more times. Errors with measuring the volume of solution could be reduced by using burettes and/or pipettes. Other answers are possible.

6 Chromatography

1–4 Your own results.

5 Your answer will depend on the inks used. Look for any black inks which did not separate into a number of colours – if the ink remained as one main dot, it was a pure colour.

6 Your answer will depend on the inks used. Similar coloured dyes in the same location on your chromatography paper are likely to contain the same chemical compound.

7 The graphite from the pencil will not dissolve in the solvent (water), so it will not interfere with the results. The pencil line is also helpful when working out the R_f values, as it gives a clear point from which to take measurements.

8 So you knew which pen/original colour of ink was used to produce each spot of ink.

9 So the water will rise up the paper and dissolves the dyes.

7 Identifying ions

Part 1

1 Your own results. (Your teacher will have the correct answers for the substances provided.)

2 To remove any substance from the previous test, since this could affect the flame colour seen in the new test.

3 Your own answer. You may have encountered various difficulties, e.g.

- faint flame colour, which made it difficult to distinguish the colour
- substances dropped into the Bunsen, making it difficult to see subsequent results
- unknown samples becoming more contaminated as tests went on.

If you encountered no difficulties, you should explain this. For example, 'I had no difficulties as I was able to correctly identify the metal ions in all five unknown solids.'

Part 2

1–2 Your own results. (Your teacher will have the correct answers for the substances provided.)

3 Aluminium ions and calcium ions both produce a white precipitate but step **D** allows you to distinguish them. Aluminium hydroxide disappears in excess sodium hydroxide solution, but calcium hydroxide does not.

Part 3

1 Your own results. (Your teacher will have the correct answers for the substances provided.)

2 The acid reacts with the carbonate ions, so silver carbonate and barium carbonate cannot form. (These substances could interfere with the results of the tests or produce false positive results.)

8 Water purification

1 Likely answers are:

	Sample	Flame test (positive metal ions)	Nitric acid/silver nitrate test (negative halide ions)
Before	Salty water	yellow indicating sodium (ions) present	white indicating chloride (ions) present
After	Distilled water	no colour change visible (various metal ions not present)	remains clear (so no halide ions present)

2 Your own answer and explanation.

3 Add the sample to white anhydrous copper(II) sulfate and it will turn blue; or apply the sample to blue cobalt(II) chloride paper and it will turn pink. Remember, however, that these tests do not tell you if the water is pure: they will only show that the sample contains water.

4 Your answer should include:

liquid is heated until it boils; liquid/water evaporates and turns into steam (water vapour); steam is pure water vapour; the steam/vapour passes into the condenser, where it cools down; as the vapour cools, it turns back into a liquid; the pure water collects as the distillate; anything dissolved in the water should remain in the conical flask.

Use this space for any rough notes, diagrams or calculations. Remember to write the practical number so that you can easily find your material.

Use this space for any rough notes, diagrams or calculations. Remember to write the practical number so that you can easily find your material.

Use this space for any rough notes, diagrams or calculations. Remember to write the practical number so that you can easily find your material.

Use this space for any rough notes, diagrams or calculations. Remember to write the practical number so that you can easily find your material.

Use this space for any rough notes, diagrams or calculations. Remember to write the practical number so that you can easily find your material.

Use this space for any rough notes, diagrams or calculations. Remember to write the practical number so that you can easily find your material.

Use this space for any rough notes, diagrams or calculations. Remember to write the practical number so that you can easily find your material.

Use this space for any rough notes, diagrams or calculations. Remember to write the practical number so that you can easily find your material.